PRESCHOOL MONEY BOOK

LEARN TO COUNT MONEY FOR TODDLERS

ECONOMICS FOR KIDS PUBLISHING

ISBN: 9798413440933

THIS BOOK BELONGS TO

We recommend adult supervision when doing this workbook, especially when the kid is using scissors.

LEARN ABOUT MONEY

People use money to buy things like

food	clothes	shelter

and to pay for services such as

get a haircut	cinema	a taxi ride

People buy things or services with

cards

checks

cellphone

bills and coins

People make money thanks to a job.
For example, you can work as

a teacher

a singer

a policeman or
policewoman

LEARN ABOUT COINS

There are 4 types of coins depending on their value

PENNY

1 CENT
President Abraham Lincoln

NICKEL

5 CENTS
President Thomas Jefferson

DIME

10 CENTS
President Franklin D Roosevelt

QUARTER

25 CENTS
President George Washington

LEARN ABOUT BILLS

There are 6 types of bills depending on their value

1$

President George Washington

5$

President Abraham Lincoln

10$

Treasury Secretary
Alexander Hamilton

20$

President Andrew Jackson

50$

President Ulysses S. Grant

100$

United States founding father
Benjamin Franklin

LET'S PLAY A BIT!!!

GRAB A PENCIL AND SOME CRAYONS

COLORING COINS GAMES

Color the penny

COLORING COINS GAMES

Color the nickel

COLORING COINS GAMES

Color the dime

COLORING COINS GAMES

Color the quarter

COLORING COINS GAMES

Color only the pennies

COLORING COINS GAMES

Color only the nickels

COLORING COINS GAMES

Color only the dimes

COLORING COINS GAMES

Color only the quarters

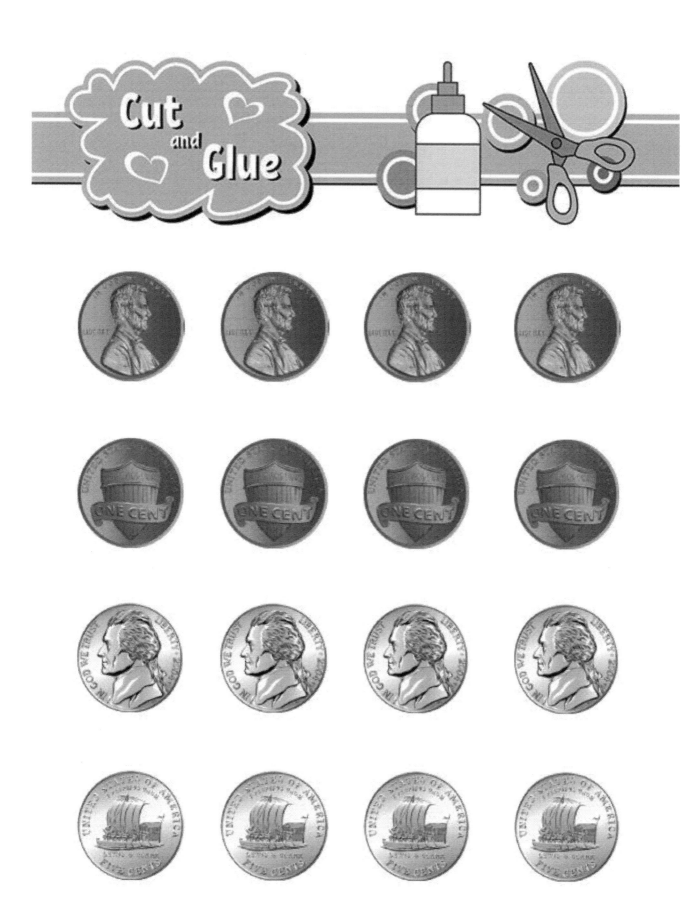

COINS SORTING GAME

Put the coins you cutted and pasted
in the corresponding piggybank

COINS VALUE LEARNING

THE VALUE OF A PEENY IS

1 CENT

Trace and write the numbers.
You will learn the value of each coin.

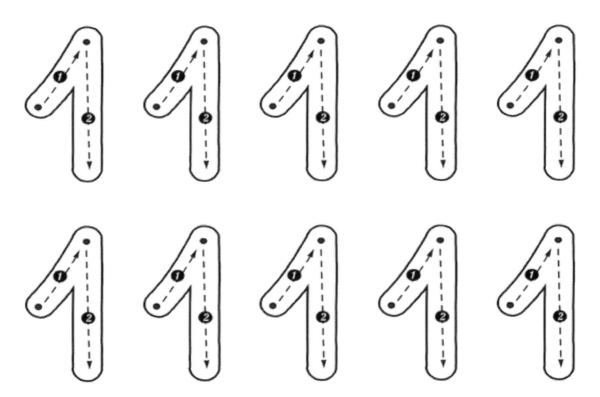

THE VALUE OF A PEENY IS

1 CENT

COINS VALUE LEARNING

THE VALUE OF A NICKEL IS

5 CENTS

Trace and write the numbers.
You will learn the value of each coin.

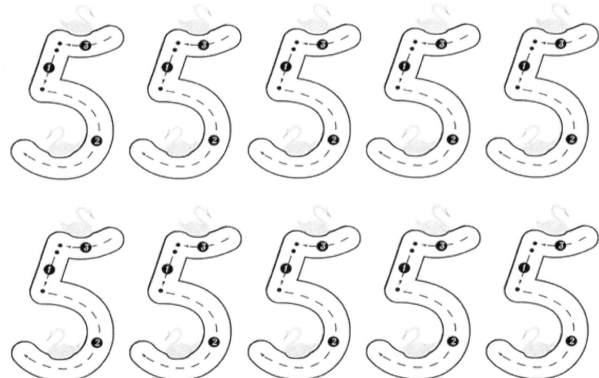

THE VALUE OF A NICKEL IS

5 CENTS

5 5 5 5 5 5 5 5 5 5 5 5

5 5 5 5 5 5 5 5 5 5 5 5

5 5 5 5 5 5 5 5 5 5 5 5

5 5 5 5 5 5

5 5 5 5 5

5 5 5 5 5

5 5 5

COINS VALUE LEARNING

THE VALUE OF A DIME IS

10 CENTS

Trace and write the numbers.
You will learn the value of each coin.

THE VALUE OF A DIME IS

10 CENTS

10 10 10 10 10 10 10

10 10 10 10 10 10 10

10 10 10 10 10 10 10

10 10 10 10

10 10 10 10

10 10 10 10

10 10

COINS VALUE LEARNING

THE VALUE OF A QUARTER IS

25 CENTS

Trace and write the numbers.
You will learn the value of each coin.

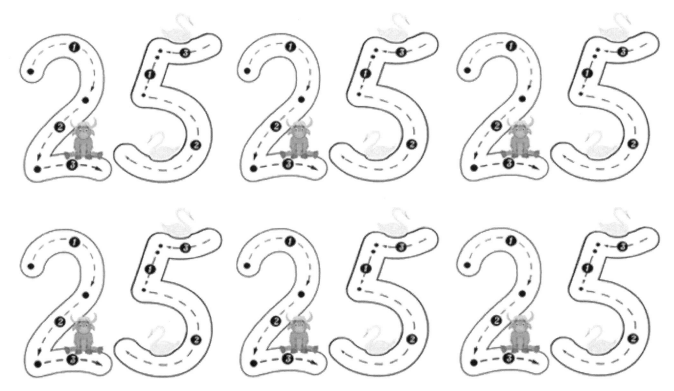

THE VALUE OF A QUARTER IS
25 CENTS

25 25 25 25 25 25

25 25 25 25 25 25

25 25 25 25 25 25

25 25 25 25

25 25 25 25

25 25 25 25

25 25

COIN MATCHING GAME

Connect the coin to the right value and color the number

COIN MATCHING GAME

Connect the coin to the right value and color the number

COIN MATCHING GAME

Connect the coin to the right value and color the number

COIN MATCHING GAME

Connect the coin to the right value and color the number

COIN MATCHING GAME

Connect each coin to the right value

BILLS COLORING GAME

Color the bills based on their values using the color code below

1$	5$	10$	20$
red	blue	yellow	green

Cut and Glue

Cut the pictures of the presidents and paste them in the correct bill

BILLS VALUE LEARNING

THE VALUE OF THIS BILL IS

$1

Trace and write

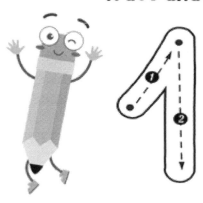

BILLS VALUE LEARNING

THE VALUE OF THIS BILL IS

$5

Trace and write

5 5 5 5 5 5 5 5 5

5 5 5 5 5

5 5 5

BILLS VALUE LEARNING

THE VALUE OF THIS BILL IS

$10

Trace and write

BILLS VALUE LEARNING

THE VALUE OF THIS BILL IS

$20

Trace and write

BILLS VALUE LEARNING

Write the value of the bill in the box

BILLS VALUE LEARNING

Write the value of the bill in the box

BILLS VALUE LEARNING

Write the value of the bill in the box

BILLS MAZES

Help the bill to find its value

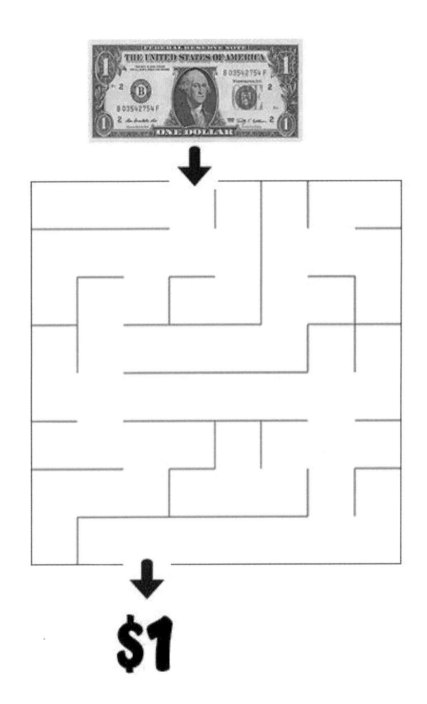

$1

BILLS MAZES

Help the bill to find its value

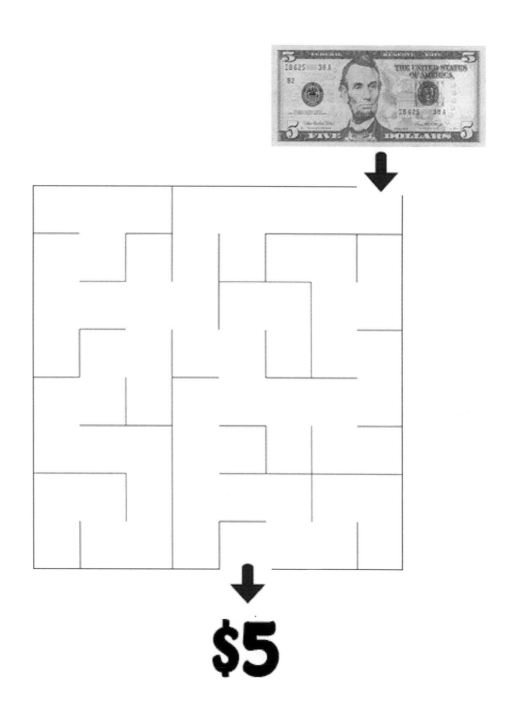

$5

BILLS MAZES

Help the bill to find its value

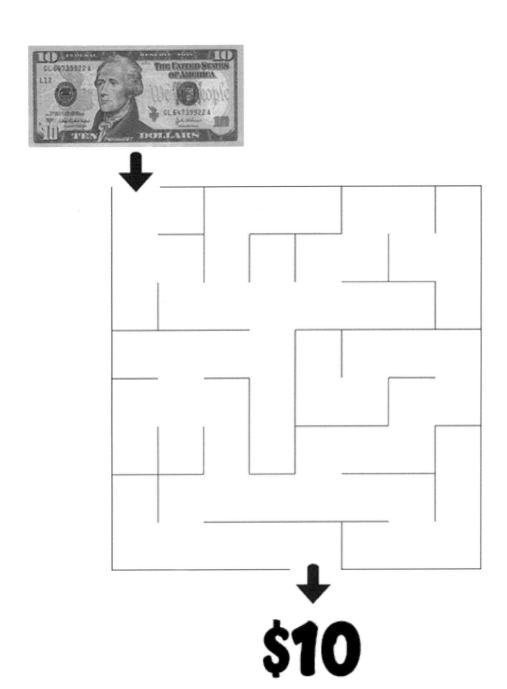

$10

BILLS MAZES

Help the bill to find its value

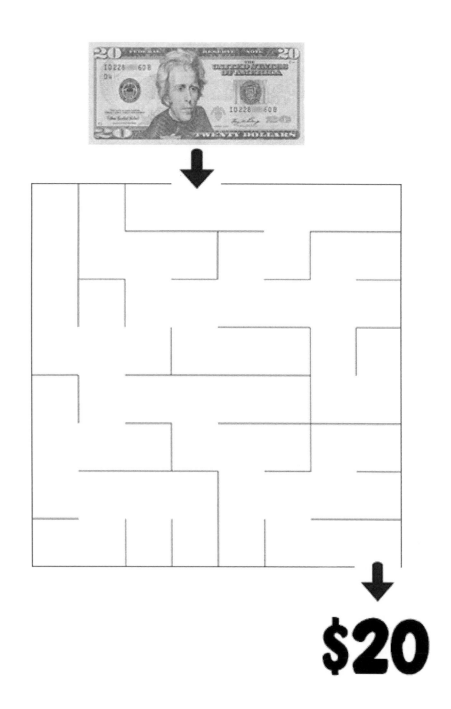

$20

LET'S GO SHOPPING

If I have one penny, what can I buy?

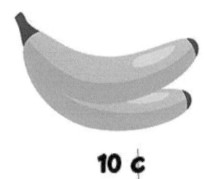

10 ¢

1 ¢

4 ¢

3 ¢

LET'S GO SHOPPING

If I have one nickel, what can I buy?

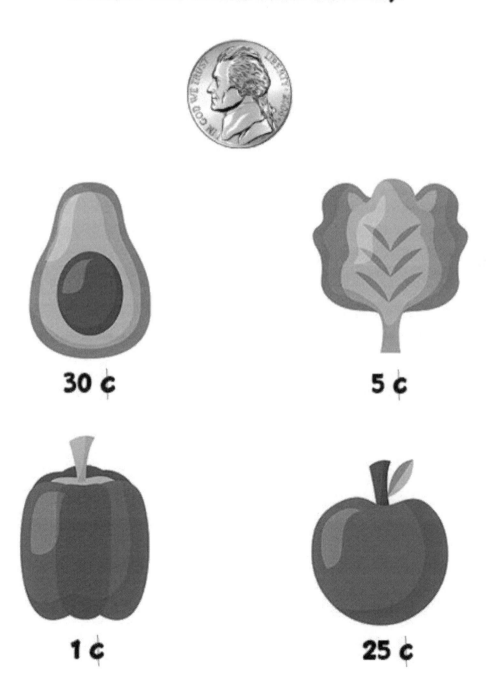

30 ¢

5 ¢

1 ¢

25 ¢

LET'S GO SHOPPING

If I have one dime, what can I buy?

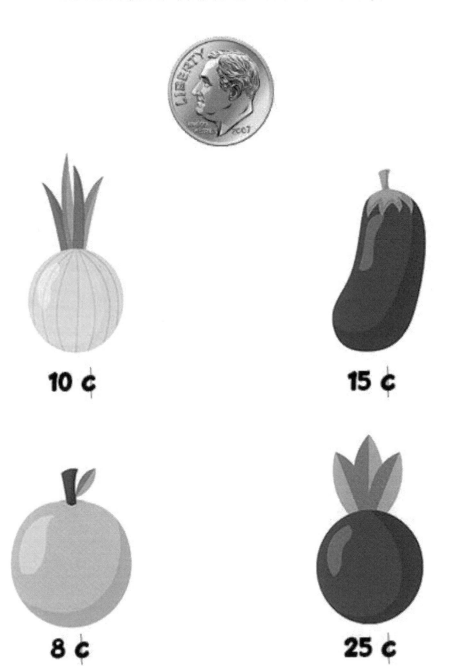

10 ¢

15 ¢

8 ¢

25 ¢

LET'S GO SHOPPING

If I have one quarter, what can I buy?

20 ¢

10 ¢

15 ¢

25 ¢

LET'S GO SHOPPING

Choose the correct bill to buy this product

$1

LET'S GO SHOPPING

Choose the correct bill to buy this product

$10

LET'S GO SHOPPING

Choose the correct bill to buy this product

$20

LET'S GO SHOPPING

Choose the correct bill to buy this product

$5

DIPLOMA

The certificate is presented to

for completing this workbook

Date

Signature